RESOURCE BANK

EXTENDING PLACE VALUE

CONTENTS

About this book

The resources provided in *Extending place value* can be used throughout Key Stage 2 to develop children's understanding of place value and the number system. The activities emphasize ways to question children and their ability to talk about numbers and read numbers. Different activities are aimed at the whole class, groups, pairs or individuals; but many of them are flexible and can be adapted to suit a particular situation. Many of the group, pair or individual activities follow on directly from a whole-class activity, and can thus be linked into a longer activity on a particular teaching focus.

Many of the activities are based on the A1 poster provided in the centre of the book. The poster is designed not only as a focal point for discussion, but also as an interactive teaching resource. The colour side uses an Olympic stadium as a context for considering very large numbers (such as crowd figures) and very small numbers (such as timings to hundredths of a second). A number grid for making large and small numbers by attaching digit cards, a set of digit cards, a net for a ten-sided dice and a chart of population statistics are given on the black and white side of the poster.

As well as lesson plans and photocopiable activity sheets, this book includes four photocopiable resource sheets (pages 4–7) which can be used to make place value 'arrow' cards for use in several of the activities. All of these resources can be photocopied, enlarged and coloured in as appropriate. It is worth making several copies of pages 4–7 on thin card as preparation for teaching this topic.

Interactive displays

Each activity incorporates ideas for classroom displays. Many of these displays can be used for further work, as a focus for discussion or mathematical investigation.

INTRODUCTION

About teaching place value

It is important for children to have a good grasp of place value in order to make estimates and check that their answers to calculations are reasonable. However, children often have difficulty in understanding the place value system. This is usually because they see written numbers, particularly larger ones, as a series of individual digits (like a telephone number) rather than as a whole number.

It is therefore important that children are always encouraged to read a number as a whole number (for example, 423 should be read as 'four hundred and twenty-three' rather than as 'four two three'). When they are working with larger numbers, encourage them to point to each digit as they read it (from the left). For example, 4525 should be read as four thousand (point to the 4), five hundred (point to the 5), twenty (point to the 2) and five (point to the 5).

More problems arise with the introduction of decimals. The children have just got used to the idea that the more digits there are, the bigger the number is. Now they discover that this is not necessarily true! It helps to use decimals in practical contexts such as money and measuring; but they will need to be able to use decimals in more abstract contexts. Other resources such as number lines and number grids (for example, a 0–99 number square) will help the children to make visual representations.

The Numeracy Hour

The introduction of a structured numeracy lesson of between 45 and 60 minutes (the 'Numeracy Hour') into many schools in England, as a result of the National Numeracy Project, has led many teachers to modify the way they teach. There is a much greater focus on whole-class interactive teaching, on the use of effective questioning, and on developing children's mental strategies. The activities in this book include a range of questions that can stimulate and guide mathematical investigation. It is also important to remember that the most effective interactive teaching depends on the teacher responding appropriately to what the children have to say.

Mental maths starters

At the beginning of each section of activities in this book, some 'starters' are provided to give an idea of the range of questions that could be used during quick-fire sessions in order to keep the children's mental maths skills simmering. It is essential to use as wide a range of vocabulary as possible. This work should be oral, perhaps using a board or flip chart to present numbers; the children should be encouraged to explain their methods. The sessions are recommended for use in the first 10 minutes or so of the 'numeracy hour', but would be good practice in any maths lesson.

Preparing to use the poster

The A1 full-colour poster shows an Olympic stadium in which numbers are used in a variety of ways: to measure time, length, crowd figures and so on. This picture is the focus of several activities, and is the starting point for much of the discussion. Each section starts with an activity which looks at the colour poster. Make sure that all the children are able to see the poster clearly and to take part in all work related to it.

A number of additional resources and mini-posters are provided on the black and white side of the A1

RESOURCE
BANK

EXTENDING PLACE VALUE

poster. The number grid can be used to rearrange digit cards in order to make various numbers according to the focus of the lesson. A set of digit cards is provided for you to photocopy, along with a net for a ten-sided dice. (The latter can be used for work on other aspects of number.) The A3 mini-poster shows a set of population statistics, which can be added to if appropriate.

Other uses of the poster

The 'Olympic stadium' poster provides a focus for discussion about the use of a range of units and instruments of measurement. It could also be used for estimation activities – for example, by asking the children to say roughly how many people there are in the crowd.

The spaces on the number grid can be used for work on a range of different number topics, including:
◆ mental strategies for addition or subtraction (by placing two- or three-digit numbers and a function sign in the boxes, and asking what happens if you change one digit or the function);
◆ addition or subtraction of negative numbers (by moving signs and numbers around within the grid).

LET'S LOOK AT THE POSTER

GROUP SIZE AND ORGANIZATION
Whole class.
DURATION
15–20 minutes.
LEARNING OBJECTIVE
To begin to understand the range of numbers used for a variety of different measurements.

DISCUSSION QUESTIONS

The 'Olympic stadium' poster; a range of different items of measuring equipment (such as a ruler, a metre stick, a dressmaker's tape measure, a sporting tape measure, a trundle wheel, a stop watch and so on); a flip chart and marker pen (or chalkboard and chalk).

WHAT TO DO

Make sure that all the children can see the poster. Talk about what it shows:
◆ Where is it set?
◆ How do you know?
◆ What happens at the Olympics?
Focus on the numbers: the crowd figures, 100m times, javelin results and so on. Discuss what each set of figures shows. Talk about what is used to measure them and the different units of measurement that are shown. For example, considering the javelin results:
◆ What units are used to measure how far the javelin has been thrown?
◆ Who threw it the furthest?
◆ What kind of distance do you think that is? Longer than the classroom? Longer than the playground?

◆ What instrument would be best to measure the throws with?
◆ Would this tape measure be long enough? (Hold up tape measure.)
Look back at the poster as a whole:
◆ Which is the largest number on the poster? How do you know?
Now look at the presenter's speech bubble. Ask a child to have a go at writing that number on the flip chart. Do the others agree?
◆ Which is the smallest number on the poster? How can you tell?
Brainstorm with the children other places in which numbers might be used at the Olympic Games. For example, on the competitors' shirts:
◆ Does the size of the number matter here?
◆ Where does the size of the number matter? Is it important in the hundred metres result?
◆ Would the highest or lowest measurement win the 100m? Why?
◆ Would the highest or lowest measurement win the javelin? Why?
Make sure that the children understand why the winning result is sometimes the lowest number (a time or position) and sometimes the highest number (a distance or weight).

Arrow cards (1)

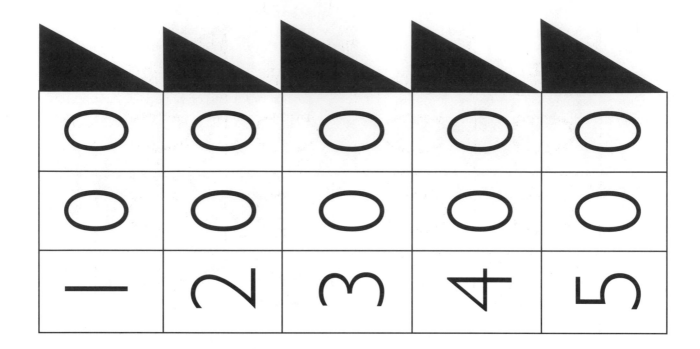

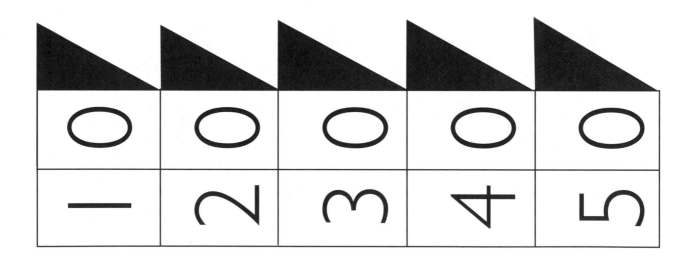

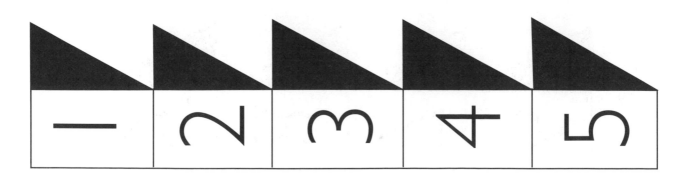

PHOTOCOPIABLE

RESOURCE BANK

EXTENDING PLACE VALUE

Arrow cards (2)

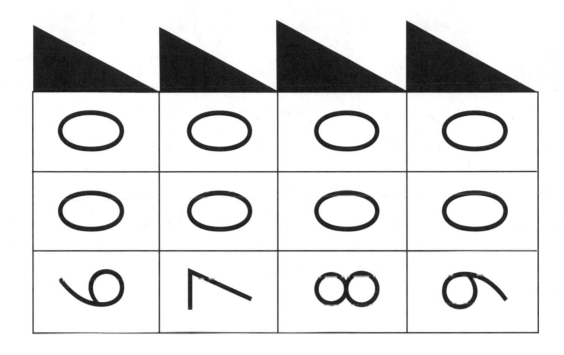

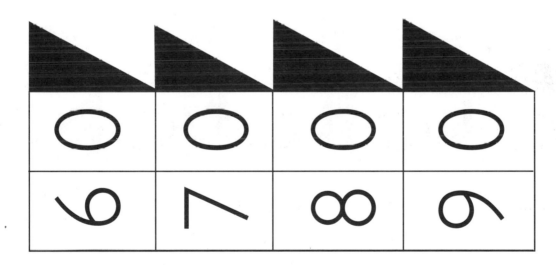

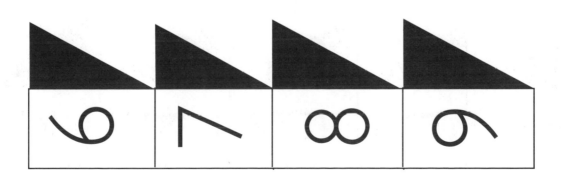

Arrow cards (3)

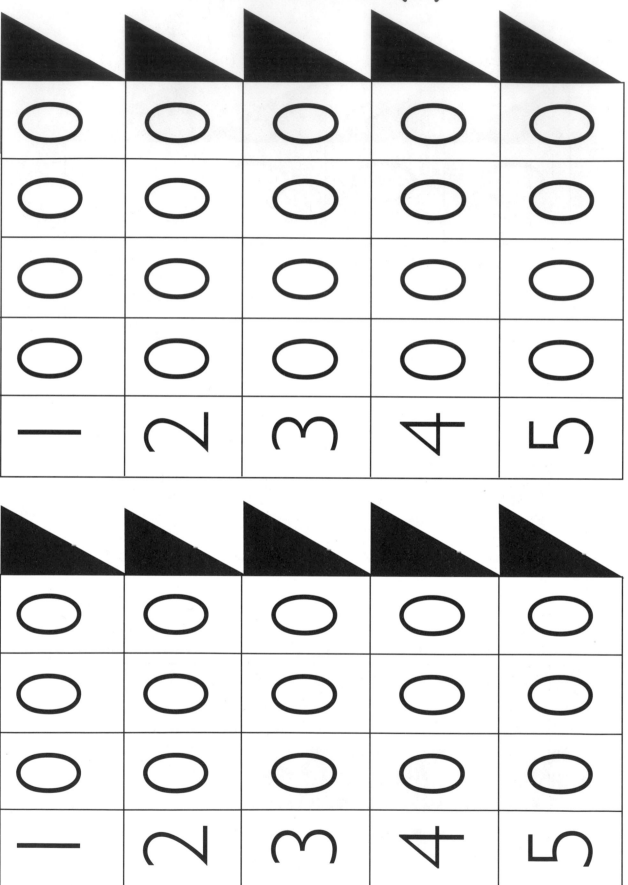

EXTENDING PLACE VALUE

Arrow cards (4)

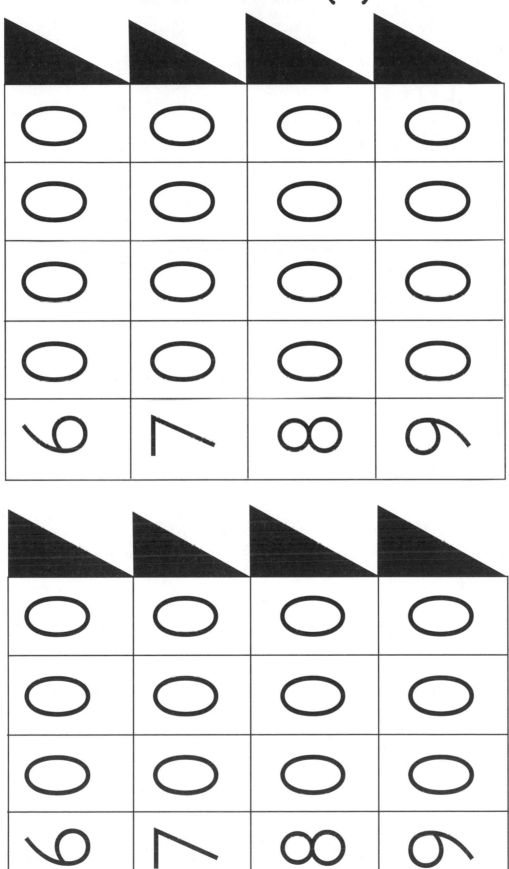

PHOTOCOPIABLE
RESOURCE
BANK

LARGE NUMBERS

Figure 1

MENTAL MATHS STARTERS

Five or six digits:
- *Write in figures the number twenty-three thousand and four.*
- *Which number is 1 more than 18 304?*
- *Which number is 1 less than 35 089?*
- *What is the value of the 3 in the number 43 798?*
- *Write the number 102 654 in words.*

Seven digits and beyond:
- *Write in figures the number twelve million, one hundred and forty-six thousand.*
- *What is 1 more than 1 400 599?*
- *Write the number that is 1 less than two million.*
- *What number is 10 more than 5 000 457?*

FIVE- AND SIX-DIGIT NUMBERS

GROUP SIZE AND ORGANIZATION
Whole class.
DURATION
20–25 minutes.
LEARNING OBJECTIVE
To read and order numbers with up to six digits.

YOU WILL NEED
The 'Olympic stadium poster', the number grid, the digit cards 0–9 (from the poster), Blu-Tack, a flip chart and marker pen (or chalkboard and chalk).

WHAT TO DO
As preparation, cover the bottom half of the black and white poster with blank paper and fix the 0–9 digits there with Blu-Tack. (See Figure 1.)

Look at the 'Olympic stadium' poster. Focus on the crowd figures. Turn the poster over and look at the number grid and the 'Large numbers' (the same numbers as the crowd figures). Tell the children that you are going to focus together on five-digit numbers.
- *Why are the numbers so large? What do they tell us?*
- *Can you find the smallest number [of the crowd figures]? Read it out. How do you know it is the smallest?*
- *Now find the largest number. Read it out. How do you know it is the largest?*

Ask a child to write the numbers on the flip chart. Talk about where the largest number might be written in relation to the smallest: above it or below it, depending on whether the numbers are being written in ascending or descending order. When they are all in order, read out the list as a class.

Ask the children to think of a number that lies in between two of the numbers in the list. Use the digit cards to make the number in the number grid.
- *Who can make a bigger number using the same digits but in different positions?*

Repeat this process several times, ending with:
- *Who can think of a number that is bigger than the largest number?*
- *Can you use the cards to show us the number?*

ASSESSMENT
Check whether the children recognize that the value of a digit changes according to its position. Give each child a strip of paper with a row of five boxes on it. Tell the children to roll a dice five times and write each number rolled in a box on the number strip. Ask each child to read out his or her five-digit number.

IDEAS FOR DISPLAY
Ask the children to find large numbers in newspapers or magazines and cut them out (this can be done as a homework task). Each number can be written on a coloured paper 'brick' along with the child's initials. To add a number to the 'large-number wall', the child must read the number to the rest of the class. Discuss whether each new number is bigger or smaller than those already displayed.

IDEAS FOR DIFFERENTIATION
Less able children could use only four-digit numbers, and start with numbers that have 0 in the hundreds, tens and units columns. More able children could go on to look at six-digit and even seven-digit numbers.

LARGE NUMBERS

PARTITIONING LARGE NUMBERS

GROUP SIZE AND ORGANIZATION
Whole class, sitting at desks or tables.
DURATION
15–20 minutes.
LEARNING OBJECTIVE
To read and partition numbers with up to five digits.

YOU WILL NEED
The number grid poster; a set of place value 'arrow' cards (copied from photocopiable pages 4–7) for each child or pair.

WHAT TO DO
Look at the number grid poster. As a class, read out the 'large numbers' written above the grid. Point to the individual digits as the children read each number, and ask what they are worth (for example, the 5 in 45 762). Make the numbers using 'arrow' cards. Ask the children to make each number and hold it up.
- *How much is the 7 worth?*
- *How many thousands are there?*

Take the hundreds card away and ask the children to read the new number.
- *What would the number be if the 10s digit was removed?* (The children will be able to see the 0 on the card beneath.)
- *What would the number be if 500 was put in the hundreds digit space?*

As the children read out each 'large number' together, ask a child or pair to change one of the digits and hold up the new number. Ask the others to say what has changed and what the new number is. Repeat this with several children.

At the end of the session, ask the children to think about how they would add 1 or 10 to a number. (See the section on pages 18–23.)

ASSESSMENT
Note those children who can select the correct cards in order to form the number, showing that they recognize the value of each digit.

IDEAS FOR DISPLAY
Put some four- or five-figure numbers on the wall, and next to them put place value cards to show what the number is made up from (for example, 2517 with the cards 2000, 500, 10 and 7). Some could be set out as vertical additions, or as questions: *Does 2000 + 500 + 10 + 7 = 2517?* Display some incorrect examples for the children to find.

IDEAS FOR DIFFERENTIATION
Less able children could work with place value cards that are colour-coded (for example, the thousands cards in green, the hundreds cards in red, and so on).

MAKING FIVE- AND SIX-DIGIT NUMBERS

GROUP SIZE AND ORGANIZATION
Pairs or individuals.
DURATION
20 minutes.
LEARNING OBJECTIVE
To read, write and order numbers with up to six digits.

YOU WILL NEED
The number grid poster; a set of 0–9 digit cards per child (photocopied from the poster), a list of number words (*one, two... hundred, thousand, million*), plain paper, pens or pencils, a flip chart and marker pen (or chalkboard and chalk).

WHAT TO DO
Put five digits in the spaces provided on the number grid. Ask the children to read the number. Now write the number in words on the board. Ask the children whether they think it has been written correctly.

Ask the children to shuffle their pack of 0–9 digit cards and lay them out face down in front of them, then pick up five cards. They should work in pairs (or individually) to make the largest and then the smallest number they can using all five digits, and write down the numbers in figures and in words. Then they should replace the digits, shuffle the cards and repeat the exercise.
- *Which numbers did you make?*

LARGE NUMBERS

◆ *Who made the largest number? And the smallest number?*
◆ *How do you know it is the largest/smallest number?* ('Because it has the largest number in the ten thousands column', 'Because it had the same number in the ten thousands column as that number, but it had a bigger number in the thousands column', and so on.)

ASSESSMENT
Note whether the children can write the numbers in words, and understand that the value of a digit depends on its position.

IDEAS FOR DISPLAY
The children can develop the 'large number wall' (see page 8) by writing out the numbers in numerals and in words, then displaying them around the wall with the question: *Can you match these words to the correct numerals?*

IDEAS FOR DIFFERENTIATION
More able children could find all the numbers they can using four cards and then five cards; they could go on to use six or more cards. Less able children could use only four cards.

ORDERING NUMBERS BEYOND SIX DIGITS

GROUP SIZE AND ORGANIZATION
Whole class, then groups of 3 or 4.
DURATION
10–15 minutes for discussion, 20 minutes for activity.
LEARNING OBJECTIVES
To read and order numbers beyond 1 million.

YOU WILL NEED
The 'Olympic stadium' poster, the population statistics mini-poster, a flip chart and marker pen (or chalkboard and chalk), photocopiable page 11, atlases with population statistics, blank paper, scissors, adhesive.

WHAT TO DO
Look at the 'Olympic' stadium' poster with the class. Do they know what 'population' means? Point out the population statistics. Ask someone to read out one of the numbers. Do the others agree with that reading? Break down the number into columns: ten millions,

millions, hundred thousands, ten thousands, thousands, hundreds, ten and units. Point to each digit in the number as it is read out.

Look at the mini-poster of population statistics, which gives the populations of ten countries.
◆ *Which country has the highest population according to these figures? What is its population?*
◆ *How do you know that figure is the highest?*
◆ *Which country has the smallest population? What is its population?*
As a class, put the countries in order according to their population and read them out together. Write their names on the flip chart as you order them.

Give each group an atlas and a copy of photocopiable page 11. Ask the children to find the missing population figures for the sheet, and then to find and add the populations of three other countries of their choice. They should then cut out the rows and order them according to size, from the smallest to the largest, before sticking them onto a sheet of paper.

Follow this up with discussion:
◆ *Which country has the smallest/largest population?*
◆ *Can anyone use the atlas to find a country with a larger population?*
◆ *Which country has the largest population of all?*
Make sure that the children read out each number as a whole number, not as a series of individual digits.

ASSESSMENT
Check to see whether the children understand that a number in the millions has seven digits, a number in the tens of millions has eight digits and a number in the hundreds of millions has nine digits.

IDEAS FOR DISPLAY
Put a map of the world on the wall, labelled with the populations of the countries the children have looked at. This could be done as part of the main activity, with the children finding out where each country is and taking turns to place a label on the map.

IDEAS FOR DIFFERENTIATION
Less able children could look initially at population figures given as whole millions (such as 7 000 000). Adapt the photocopiable sheet to show populations in millions and half millions, and fill in the blank spaces so that the children only have to order the numbers.

More able children could find the populations of more countries, or of countries with population figures in a given range (for example, 50–75 million). They could try to approximate these population statistics to the nearest million. Can they say why the figures are given to the nearest thousand, rather than in full?

Name ——————————————   Date ——————————————

Ordering large numbers

◆ Find and fill in the missing population figures.

◆ Add figures for three more countries of your choice.

◆ Cut out the rows and put them in order of size, from the smallest population figure to the largest.

Argentina	33 778 000
Australia	17 663 000
Belgium	10 046 000
Columbia	33 951 000
Denmark	5 189 000
France	57 660 000
Italy	57 057 000
Kenya	28 113 000
Russia	
United Kingdom	
United States of America	

ROUNDING WITH LARGE NUMBERS

THE NEAREST THOUSAND

GROUP SIZE AND ORGANIZATION
Whole class.
DURATION
15–20 minutes.
LEARNING OBJECTIVE
To round large numbers to the nearest hundred, thousand or ten thousand.

YOU WILL NEED

The 'Olympic stadium' poster, the number grid, a flip chart and marker pen (or chalkboard and chalk).

WHAT TO DO

Look at the 'Olympic stadium' poster with the class, focusing on the crowd figures.

◆ What information do these figures give us?
◆ How important is it that they are exact? Do they need to count everybody?
◆ Would a rough estimate do?
◆ What sort of estimate?
◆ To the nearest ten, hundred, thousand? Why?

Turn the poster over and ask the children to read out the 'large numbers' again, either as a class or in groups. Then look at the number 46 917.

◆ What number is that nearly?

Allow the children to make a range of responses. They may suggest 46 000, 47 000, 50 000 or other numbers.

◆ What is it to the nearest thousand?
◆ Is it closer to 46 000 or 47 000?

◆ How do you know?

As a class, count up in ten thousands to 100 000, then count back down. Ask the children:

◆ What is 46 917 to the nearest ten thousand?
◆ How do you know?
◆ Which other numbers from the list can be rounded to 50 000?

Look at the numbers that can be rounded to 50 000 and write them on the board or flip chart. Ask individual children to come out and write next to each of the numbers its nearest thousand. Explain that it might sometimes be more appropriate to round to the nearest hundred. Look at the crowd figures and discuss with the children whether it is appropriate to give these to the nearest hundred or thousand, and why. Look at 46 917:

◆ What is its nearest hundred?
◆ Which two hundreds does it lie in between?

Look at the numbers on the flip chart again. Ask individual children to write each number to the nearest hundred. Ask more children to think of other numbers that can be rounded to the same hundred, and to write them on the board. Discuss the range of numbers that could be rounded to the same hundred (from 50 below to 49 above). Emphasize the idea that '5 rounds up', and thus that a number ending in 50 will round **up** to the nearest hundred. Give some examples:

◆ Rounding to the nearest hundred, 450 would round to? 346 would round to? 1250 would round to?
◆ What is the smallest number that would round up to 3000 if you were rounding to the nearest thousand?

ASSESSMENT

Note whether the children are able to round up as well as down. Note whether they understand that when rounding numbers, they need to look for the hundred or thousand that is nearest.

ROUNDING WITH LARGE NUMBERS

IDEAS FOR DISPLAY

Ask the children to round the numbers from the 'large number wall' to the nearest thousand. Add bricks with four-figure numbers to the wall and ask the children to move these bricks around so that they are positioned next to a brick that has the nearest thousand on it. This could be done as a whole class warm-up activity or plenary session.

IDEAS FOR DIFFERENTIATION

Less able children could round only to the nearest thousand. More able children could try rounding to the nearest ten. They may find this more challenging with a larger number of digits.

ROUNDING TO A GIVEN NUMBER

GROUP SIZE AND ORGANIZATION
Groups of 3 or 4.
DURATION
20–25 minutes.
LEARNING OBJECTIVE
To recognize numbers that could be rounded to a given thousand or ten thousand.

YOU WILL NEED

The number grid poster, a set of digit cards 0–9 for each group, paper, pencils.

WHAT TO DO

Use the number grid poster to recap on the idea of rounding. Remind the children that when you are rounding to the nearest hundred, 50 is rounded up and 49 is rounded down. When you are rounding to the nearest thousand, 500 is rounded up and 499 is rounded down.

Give each group a different starting number to round to (these could be written on cards and given out), for example 35 000. Tell the children that they have to use five of their number cards to make as many five-digit numbers as possible that can be rounded to 35 000. They may choose the five digits they want to use; but once they have chosen them, they can't change them. They should write down all the suitable numbers they make. When a group think they cannot find any more numbers, they should swap with another group and see whether they can find any more.

Follow up by asking: *Which digits made the most numbers that could be rounded to the given total?* The strategy of picking the ten thousands and thousands digits, one less than the thousands digit, one digit above 5 and one below 5 would enable them to find at least eight solutions.

At the end of the lesson, ask the children about the range of numbers that can be rounded to a given thousand. Discuss why it is useful to be able to round numbers to the nearest hundred, thousand and so on. For example, in the Olympic stadium they don't need to know the exact crowd figure: only an approximate number for catering, security and so on. With population statistics, it is difficult to be exact because of continual change.

ASSESSMENT

Note whether the children can recognize numbers that would be rounded to a given thousand or ten thousand, and can recognize when a number is closer to one thousand than another.

IDEAS FOR DISPLAY

Choose a 'thousand [or ten thousand] of the week'. Ask the children to bring in numbers cut out of magazines or newspapers that can be rounded to that number. (Car and house prices are useful for this.) Make a wall display of the numbers.

IDEAS FOR DIFFERENTIATION

Less able children could work with four-digit numbers. More able children could work with six-digit numbers, and try rounding to the nearest hundred.

One careful owner. About 5000 miles on clock. Yours for only £4999

ROUNDING WITH LARGE NUMBERS

THE NEAREST MILLION

GROUP SIZE AND ORGANIZATION
Whole class.
DURATION
20–25 minutes.
LEARNING OBJECTIVES
To round numbers to the nearest hundred thousand or million.

YOU WILL NEED
The population statistics mini-poster.

WHAT TO DO
Look at the population statistics mini-poster. Point to the name of a country and ask a child to read out its population. Do the others agree with the reading? Go through several examples. Ask:
◆ *Which country has a population of about 8 million?*
◆ *Are there any other countries that have a similar-sized population?*
◆ *What is the population of Canada/Brazil to the nearest million?*
Go down the list of countries on the poulation statistics mini-poster, pointing to each country and asking the children to say (together) what its population is to the nearest million.
◆ *Were some of them more difficult to work out than others? Which ones?*
◆ *Why do you think that might be?*
◆ *What other approximation could we make?* The children may suggest rounding to the nearest ten thousand, hundred thousand or ten million.
◆ *If we rounded to the nearest ten million, which of the countries would round to the same ten million?*
Write the population figures on the flip chart. Ask individual children to come up and write each population figure to the nearest hundred thousand. Check whether the rest of the class agree.

Discuss which amount it is most appropriate to round to, and whether this is the same for all countries.

ASSESSMENT
Check whether the children are able to round to the nearest hundred thousand or the nearest million, and that they recognize when to round up and when to round down.

IDEAS FOR DISPLAY
Develop the map of the world display (see page 10) by rounding the population of each labelled country to the nearest ten million. Use a key and coloured stickers to mark each country according to what figure its population figure is rounded to.

IDEAS FOR DIFFERENTIATION
Less able children could work with a set of numbers that all have the same number of digits. More able children could work with a wider-ranging set of numbers, and round to the nearest ten thousand as well.

MAKING CONNECTIONS

GROUP SIZE AND ORGANIZATION
Pairs.
DURATION
20–25 minutes.
LEARNING OBJECTIVES
To round numbers to the nearest hundred thousand or million. To use this information to recognize relationships between given numbers.

YOU WILL NEED
The population statistics mini-poster, photocopiable page 16, atlases, blank paper, pens or pencils.

WHAT TO DO
Arrange the class into pairs. Look together at the population statistics mini-poster. Ask questions which require the children to use approximation skills:
◆ *What is the population of Austria to the nearest million?* (8 million.)
◆ *What is the population of Germany to the nearest ten million?* (80 million.)
◆ *Roughly how many times bigger than the population of Austria is the population of Germany?* (Ten times.)
◆ *What is the relationship between the population of Mexico and that of Norway?* (The population of Mexico is twice that of Norway.)
◆ *What other relationships can you find?*
Give each pair a copy of photocopiable page 16, a sheet of blank paper and an atlas. Tell the children that rounding will help them to find the connections between the different population figures. They need to use the information in the table and the atlas to answer the questions on the sheet.

At the end of the lesson, go through some of the questions. The answers the children should have found

ROUNDING WITH LARGE NUMBERS

from the table alone are: **1.** Austria and Mexico; **2.** India; **3.** Two times bigger.

ASSESSMENT
Note which children can use appropriate estimates in order to see the connections between the sizes of different populations. Photocopiable page 16 could be used as an assessment task.

IDEAS FOR DISPLAY
Around the world map display, put up questions about the relationships between the populations of different countries – for example: *How many times bigger than the population of Canada is the population of Egypt?*

IDEAS FOR DIFFERENTIATION
Give less able children fewer countries to look at and closed questions (such as the first three on page 16). Ask more able children to look at the relationship between population size and the area of the country.

CROWDED OUT!

> ### GROUP SIZE AND ORGANIZATION
> Individuals.
> ### DURATION
> 15–20 minutes.
> ### LEARNING OBJECTIVE
> To round numbers to the nearest thousand in order to find approximate totals.

YOU WILL NEED
The 'Olympic stadium' poster, photocopiable page 17, blank paper, pens or pencils.

WHAT TO DO
Look together at the crowd figures displayed on the 'Olympic stadium' poster. Handwritten numbers like these often use commas. Check that the children do not think they are decimal points: would thousands or decimals be more sensible here? Ask a child to read out the figures for Monday and Tuesday of the first week. Ask: *How could you calculate the approximate total for the two days to the nearest thousand?* Encourage the children to round the numbers before adding them. Then ask: *Which two days have a total of approximately 150 000? How did you work it out?*

Give each child a copy of photocopiable page 17, giving the crowd figures for two weeks, and a sheet of blank paper. Ask them to answer the questions – all of

which require them to make approximations first.

The answers are: **1. (a)** 158 000 **(b)** 98 000 **(c)** 113 000 **(d)** 120 000 **(e)** 100 000 **(f)** 137 000 **2.** Monday week 1 and Saturday week 2 **3.** Tuesday week 1 and Friday week 1 **4. (a)** Wednesday week 1 + Saturday week 1; Friday week 1 + Friday week 2; Tuesday week 2 + Thursday week 2 **(b)** Tuesday week 2 and Thursday week 2 **5.** several answers are possible (for example, Tuesday, Wednesday and Saturday in week 2) **6. (a)** week 1 **(b)** 367 000.

ASSESSMENT
Note which children can round numbers to the nearest thousand and can use this information to calculate approximate totals.

IDEAS FOR DISPLAY
Put questions around the 'large number wall' that encourage the children to make approximations for calculation – for example: *Which two numbers have a total of approximately 10 000? Which two numbers when added together give the largest total?*

IDEAS FOR DIFFERENTIATION
Less able children could calculate totals to the nearest ten thousand. More able children could find totals to the nearest hundred, or write and then swap their own questions about the crowd figures.

Name _____   Date _____

Population comparisons

◆ Use the information in this table to answer the questions below. Write your answers on another sheet.

Country	Population
Austria	7 712 000
Germany	79 479 000
Morocco	25 698 000
India	849 638 000
Canada	27 300 000
Mexico	8 237 000
Norway	4 242 000
Egypt	54 688 000
Brazil	146 000 000
Japan	123 921 000

1. Which two countries have the same population to the nearest million?
2. Which country has a population approximately 10 times bigger than Germany's?
3. Approximately how many times bigger than the population of Canada is the population of Egypt?

◆ Now use an atlas and the table to help you answer these questions.

4. Find two other countries that have a population the same as Egypt's to the nearest 10 million.
5. Name three countries that have a population approximately half the size of that of Brazil.
6. Find 2 countries whose total population is approximately the same as that of Japan.
7. How many countries can you find that have a population about half the size of Norway's?

PHOTOCOPIABLE
RESOURCE BANK

ROUNDING WITH LARGE NUMBERS

Name ——————————————— Date ———————————

Crowd figures

WEEK 1		WEEK 2	
Monday	102 614	Monday	54 712
Tuesday	46 917	Tuesday	51 168
Wednesday	52 000	Wednesday	60 913
Thursday	71 026	Thursday	48 964
Friday	45 762	Friday	53 787
Saturday	47 800	Saturday	89 478

◆ Use the information in the table to answer the questions below. Find the answers to the nearest thousand. Write them on another sheet.

1. Find the total of the two
   (a) Mondays   **(b)** Tuesdays

   (c) Wednesdays   **(d)** Thursdays

   (e) Fridays   **(f)** Saturdays

2. Find the two days that when added together give the highest total.

3. Find the two days that when added together give the lowest total.

4. **(a)** Write down all the pairs of days that have a total of about 100 000 (for example, Wednesday week 1 + Saturday week 1).

   (b) Which pair of days have the total closest to 100 000?

5. Find three days that have a total of 200 000.

6. **(a)** Which week had a greater number of people through the gate?

   (b) What was the approximate total for that week?

ADDING 1, 10, 100 AND 1000

MENTAL MATHS STARTERS
You may find that some preparatory work is needed before you can use these questions to sharpen the children's mental skills at the start of a lesson.
◆ Add 10 to 1428.
◆ What is 100 more than 3067?
◆ Find the total of 34 056 and 9.
◆ How much is 30 more than 20 017?
◆ What is 99 more than 2638?
◆ Add 2000 to 34 145.
◆ Find the sum of 999 and 5344.

ADD 1, 10 OR 100

GROUP SIZE AND ORGANIZATION
Whole class.
DURATION
15–20 minutes.
LEARNING OBJECTIVES
To add 1, 10 or 100 to any five-digit number. To adjust this skill in order to add 9 or 99.

YOU WILL NEED
The 'Olympic stadium' poster, the number grid, a set of digit cards 0–9 (photocopied from the poster), a flip chart and marker pen (or chalkboard and chalk), Blu-Tack, blank paper, pens or pencils.

WHAT TO DO
Look together at the 'Olympic stadium' poster. Focus on the crowd figures. *If one more person came on each day, what would the new figure be?* Scribe the children's answers on the flip chart. Point to each new number and ask the class to read it out.
Turn the poster over. Use the digit cards to put one of the five-digit 'large numbers' onto the number grid. Ask the children to read out this number together.
◆ What is 1 more than the number?
◆ What is 10 more than the number?
◆ How did you work it out?
Some children will still be counting on in ones. Talk to them about using a better method: you are adding one more ten to the tens column. Ask a child to come up and point to the tens column. If we add one more ten, the number in the tens column increases by 1. Change the digit card in the tens column to make the number 10 bigger. Do the same with other digits.

Point to the other 'large numbers' above the number grid, and ask the children to say what 10 more than each of these numbers is.
◆ How do you think we could add 100? Go round the class, asking individuals to add 100 to each number.
◆ Can anybody think of a quick way to add 9? Encourage the children to do this by adding 10 and subtracting 1. Write some numbers of different sizes (two to five digits) on the flip chart. Go round the class, asking children to add 9 to each number. Check that the other children agree with each answer.
◆ Can anybody add 99?
◆ How did you do it?
It is likely that someone will come up with the strategy 'add 100 and subtract 1'. If other strategies are suggested, some discussion could develop about which is the most effective and why.
Ask the children to add 99 to each of the numbers written on the flip chart within a given time limit, writing down their answers. They could check each other's answers.

ASSESSMENT
Check whether the children can add 1, 10 and 100 to a whole number using an appropriate strategy, and can use this information to add 9 and 99.

IDEAS FOR DISPLAY
Put questions or instructions around the 'large number wall' such as *What is 10 more than each of these numbers?* or *Choose five numbers on the wall and add 99 to each of them.*

IDEAS FOR DIFFERENTIATION
Less able children could work with a smaller number of digits and/or stick to adding 1, 10 and 100. More able children could go on to add 8, 98 or 102, using appropriate compensation strategies. **NB** It is very important that the children talk about their strategies.

ADDING 1, 10, 100 AND 1000

MORE ADDING 1, 10 OR 100

GROUP SIZE AND ORGANIZATION
Individuals.
DURATION
20–25 minutes.
LEARNING OBJECTIVE
To add 1, 10 or 100 to any whole number.

YOU WILL NEED
The number grid poster, a set of digit cards 0–9 per child (photocopied fromn the poster), Blu-Tack, a flip chart and marker pen (or chalkboard and chalk), photocopiable page 22, pens or pencils.

WHAT TO DO
Make one copy per child of photocopiable page 22, marked with the number of digits you want the children to work with (it is assumed that most children will use five digits here).

Look together at the number grid poster. Recap on the previous activity by asking individuals to add 1, 10 or 100 to each 'large number' you point at. Ask: *How did you do it?* Now spread out a set of 0–9 digit cards, face up. Ask a child to pick up five cards from the set and arrange them to make a number on the grid.

◆ *What is the number?*

◆ *What will the number be if I add 1 to it?*

Ask a child to come up and write the new number on the flip chart.

◆ *What if I add 10 to the original number: what will the new number be?*

Ask another child to come and write the new number on the flip chart. Check whether the other children think it has been written accurately.

◆ *What if I add 100 to the original number: what will the new number be?*

◆ *Does everybody agree?*

Give out copies of photocopiable page 22. Tell the children that they are going to pick five (or whatever number you have chosen) cards from a set of digit cards to make a number; fill in a row on the sheet by adding 1, 10 and 100 to their number; then repeat the process until the grid is complete. Ask the children to check each other's work. Discuss any difficulties that arise. For example: *What about if we add 10 to 23 897? Which number changes? Is it only the number in the tens column that changes? Why not?*

ASSESSMENT
Note whether the children can add 1, 10 or 100 to a whole number. In particular, check that they understand what happens when the digit in the relevant column is 9.

IDEAS FOR DISPLAY
Put five digit cards on the wall to make a number. At the beginning or end of a session, ask individuals to add 10 or 100 to the number and show the result using digit cards.

IDEAS FOR DIFFERENTIATION
Less able children could start by adding 1, 10 or 100 to three- or four-digit numbers. More able children could go on to add 9, 99 or 999.

ADDING 1, 10, 100 AND 1000

ADDING ON TENS OR HUNDREDS

GROUP SIZE AND ORGANIZATION
Whole class.
DURATION
15–20 minutes.
LEARNING OBJECTIVE
To add a multiple of 10 or 100 to a given whole number.

YOU WILL NEED
The number grid poster, some digit cards, Blu-Tack, a ten-sided dice (the net on the poster can be used, and perhaps enlarged, for this pupose).

WHAT TO DO
Look at the number grid poster with the children. Use digit cards to put the population figure for Austria (7 712 000) onto the number grid.
◆ *All the populations are rounded to the nearest what?* (Thousand.)
◆ *If the actual population of Austria were 7 712 326, how would we change the number to show this?* Ask a child to come up and change the necessary digits on the poster.
◆ *What is the population increased by 20? How has the number changed?* Ask a child to come up and change the digit in the tens column.
◆ *What about if we add 400? How will the number change now?* Ask a child to come up and change the digit in the hundreds column.

Divide the class into two groups. Give one group a ten-sided dice. The first child in this group rolls the dice for a multiple of 10 – for example, if 6 is thrown, 60 should be added. The first child from the other group

then has to add 60 to the number on the grid and change the appropriate digit(s). Now the dice is rolled for a multiple of 100. Alternate between adding a multiple of 10 and adding a multiple of 100. Record each new number on the flip chart. Continue until all the children have had a go at either rolling or changing the number. After each number change, ask the class to decide whether the change made is correct.

At the end of the lesson, ask: *Can you work out how much has been added on altogether?* (The children should look at the flip chart.)

ASSESSMENT
Note whether the children can add a given multiple of 10 or 100 to a whole number, especially when more than one digit is affected.

IDEAS FOR DISPLAY
Add more questions to the 'large number wall', such as *How would you add 30 to these numbers?* or *What is 500 more than each of these numbers?*

IDEAS FOR DIFFERENTIATION
Less able children could start with a smaller number. More able children could try adding on 'near-multiples' of 10 or 100: 39, 51, 199 and so on.

ADDING MORE MULTIPLES

GROUP SIZE AND ORGANIZATION
Whole class, then groups of 3 or 4.
DURATION
20–25 minutes.
LEARNING OBJECTIVE
To add a multiple of 10 or 100 to a given whole number.

YOU WILL NEED
The number grid poster, a flip chart and marker pen (or chalkboard and chalk), blank paper, pens or pencils. For each group: a copy of photocopiable page 23, a ten-sided dice (see previous activity).

WHAT TO DO
Write a five-digit number on the board. Roll a ten-sided dice to give a multiple of 10 – for example, if you roll a 7, ask the children to add 70 to the number on the board and write down their answer.

ADDING 1, 10, 100 AND 1000

◆ *What was the answer?*
◆ *Did anybody get anything different?*
◆ *How can we check which answer is correct?*
Give each group a copy of photocopiable page 23. Ask them to add four more large numbers of their own to those already on the sheet (these could be four-, five- or six-digit numbers, depending on the ability of the children). They should take turns to roll a ten-sided dice and add on the multiple of 10 to a number. Each child in the group should write down an answer; when they all agree, they can write it down on the group sheet. They should continue until the 'Multiple of 10 column' is full. How quickly can they do it?

Next, they should roll a dice for multiples of 100 and fill in the appropriate column on the sheet.

Check through each group's answers with the class.

ASSESSMENT
Note whether the children can add multiples of 10 or 100 accurately to a given number.

IDEAS FOR DIFFERENTIATION
Less able children could use fewer numbers or numbers with fewer digits. More able children could go on to add 'near multiples' of 10 or 100 – for example, if 7 is thrown, they could add 69 or 71.

EXTENSION WORK
Set up a poster puzzle. Using digit cards, put a large number on the grid. At the end of the session, change the number by adding or subtracting a multiple of 10 or 100 (without writing it down). Ask the children to tell you what number has been added or subtracted.

EVEN MORE MULTIPLES

GROUP SIZE AND ORGANIZATION
Whole class, then pairs.
DURATION
20 minutes.
LEARNING OBJECTIVES
To add a multiple of 10 or 100 to a given whole number.

YOU WILL NEED
A set of place value 'arrow' cards for each child (photocopied from pages 4–7), a set of cards with multiples of 10 and 100 written on (these could be adapted from the 'arrow' cards), a flip chart and marker pen (or chalkboard and chalk).

WHAT TO DO
Make sure all the children are facing you. Have the place value cards divided up into piles of units, tens, hundreds, thousands and ten thousands. Ask a child to come and pick a card from each pile, then make the appropriate number from the cards chosen. Ask the class to read out the number. Write the number on the flip chart.

Ask another child to pick a card from the set of cards showing multiples of 10 and 100. Write the multiple on the flip chart next to the first number in a sum – for example, 53 612 + 50 =
◆ *How will the number change when I add 50 to it?*
◆ *Who can use their cards to make the new number?*
Ask a child to come up and show the rest of the class. Check whether the others agree.

Ask the children to work in pairs. One child makes the number and picks the multiple, then hands it to his or her partner to perform the calculation; both children write down the sum and the answer. They should take turns in each role.

ASSESSMENT
Note whether the children can add multiples of 10 and 100 to any whole number.

IDEAS FOR DISPLAY
Put a selection of 'arrow' cards on the wall with some questions, such as:
◆ *How many numbers can you make using these cards?*
◆ *What is 80 more than each number?*
◆ *What is 300 more than each number?*
Put a large grid up on the wall for children to write answers.

IDEAS FOR DIFFERENTIATION
Less able children could work with three- or four-digit numbers, and/or only add multiples of 10. More able children could go on to add 'near multiples' (see above) of 10, 100 or 1000.

Name _____ Date _____

Adding 1, 10 and 100

◆ Complete the table below.
In each space in the first column, put a number with ___ digits.
Then add 1, 10 and 100 to it. The first one has been done for you.

	+ 1	+ 10	+ 100
24 675	24 676	24 685	24 775

PHOTOCOPIABLE
RESOURCE BANK

Name _____   Date _____

Adding multiples of 10 and 100

◆ Complete the table. Roll a ten-sided dice each time to decide what multiple will be added.

Number	Multiple of 10 to add	Total	Multiple of 100 to add	Total
46 9.17				
52 000				
71 026				
45 762				
47 800				
102 614				

PHOTOCOPIABLE
RESOURCE
BANK

ORDERING DECIMALS

MENTAL MATHS STARTERS
- *Listen to these numbers: 1.2, 1.07, 1.3. Which is the biggest?*
- *10.7, 10.8, 10.9 – write down the next number in the sequence.*
- *Put these numbers in order of size, smallest to largest: 2.4, 2.05, 2.36.*
- *Write 2.5 metres in centimetres.*
- *What is 347 centimetres in metres?*

INTRODUCING DECIMALS

GROUP SIZE AND ORGANIZATION
Whole class.
DURATION
15–20 minutes.
LEARNING OBJECTIVE
To recognize decimal numbers.

YOU WILL NEED
The 'Olympic stadium' poster, two 1m sticks (both with a mark every 10cm, dividing the stick into tenths).

WHAT TO DO
Look at the 'Olympic stadium' poster with the children. Point to the race that has just finished.
- *What is this race?* (The 100m, according to the score board displayed above the track.)
- *How big is 1m?* Encourage the children to show an estimated length using their arms or pointing to something that is about 1m high or wide.
- *How could I check that it is 1m?* The children may suggest a tape measure or metre rule.
Hold up a metre rule. Get two children to hold it up in front of the class, one at each end.
- *If something is smaller than 1m, what unit could I use to measure it?* (Centimetres.)
- *How many centimetres are in 1m?*
Look at the metre rule and ask the children what they notice about it. They should notice the marks dividing it into ten equal parts.
- *How many bits is the ruler divided into?* (Ten.)
- *So each part is one what of a metre?* (One tenth.)
Show the children how we can write that as a fraction ($\frac{1}{10}$) or as a decimal (0.1). The column after the decimal point is called the tenths column.
- *Who can tell me how many centimetres there are in 0.1m?* (Ten.)

- *What fraction is three parts of the metre?* (Three tenths.)
Ask a child to come and write $\frac{3}{10}$ on the flip chart.
- *What would that be as a decimal?* (0.03) *Can you write it on the flip chart?*
- *How many centimetres are there in 0.3m?* (30cm)
Repeat this with eight tenths and then five tenths. Point out that 0.5 = ½.
Now ask another pair of children to hold up another metre stick.
- *Who can show me how much 1.2 metres would be? What about 1.7 metres?* Check to see that the other children agree.
   At the end of the session, reinforce the idea that the numbers after the decimal point are parts of one, just as the tenths of a metre are parts of 1m.

ASSESSMENT
Check whether the children can recognize and begin to use decimal numbers. They could do this by measuring things around the room in metres or by drawing lines of given lengths on the playground.

IDEAS FOR DISPLAY
When a child has measured a particular item, such as the door or the bookshelf, he or she could put a label on it with its height or length in metres (to one decimal place).

IDEAS FOR DIFFERENTIATION
More able children could measure to the nearest centimetre or millimetre, giving a two- or three-place decimal.

ORDERING DECIMALS

ORDERING DECIMALS

GROUP SIZE AND ORGANIZATION
Whole class.
DURATION
20–25 minutes.
LEARNING OBJECTIVE
To order decimal numbers with one decimal place.

YOU WILL NEED
The 'Olympic stadium' poster.

WHAT TO DO
Use the 'Olympic stadium' poster as a context for looking at decimals.
◆ *What is a decimal number?*
◆ *Where can you see them on the poster?*
Stress that the numbers after the decimal point are parts of one unit. Use the idea of money or measures to explain tenths and hundredths. Explain that we normally show hundredths (pence) in money, even if the hundreds digit is 0, because the 1p is a familiar unit.

Ask the children to tell you all the numbers on the poster which have only one digit after the decimal point. Write these down on the board. Then say that the numbers need to be put in order from the smallest to the largest.
◆ *How are we going to do this?*
◆ *Which digit has the highest value?*
Remind the children that they will need to look first at the numbers before the decimal point, then at the tenths. Take suggestions for the order of the numbers., checking each time whether the other children agree:
◆ *Do you think that is right?*
◆ *Does anybody think it should be something else?*
When all the numbers are in order, choose two numbers that are next to each other. Ask the children to think of a number that could go in between these two numbers. Do this several times.

ASSESSMENT
Note whether the children can order the decimal numbers correctly.

IDEAS FOR DISPLAY
Ask the children to cut out decimal numbers from newspapers and magazines at home: money, interest rates, temperatures and so on. These can be displayed on bricks on the number wall.

IDEAS FOR DIFFERENTIATION
For less able children, identify the required numbers on the poster. For more able children, include whole numbers as well as decimal numbers for the ordering task.

MORE ORDERING DECIMALS

GROUP SIZE AND ORGANIZATION
Whole class, then individuals.
DURATION
20–25 minutes.
LEARNING OBJECTIVE
To order decimal numbers with one decimal place.

YOU WILL NEED
A flip chart and marker pen (or chalk and chalkboard). For each child: a set of digit cards 0–4, a ten-sided dice, a copy of photocopiable page 28.

0	1	2	3	4	5

Figure 2

WHAT TO DO
Draw a 0–5 number line on the flip chart (as shown in Figure 2). Ask a child to pick a card at random from his or her pack of 0–4 digit cards. Ask another child to roll the ten-sided dice. If the first child picks a 2 and the second rolls a 7, write the number 2.7 on the flip chart. Repeat this twice, so there are three numbers on the flip chart.

Now ask: *Where on my number line will 2.7 go?* Ask a child to come up and mark it on the line. Talk about why it goes there. Check that the other children agree with the position marked. Repeat with the other numbers.

ORDERING DECIMALS

Give out copies of photocopiable page 28. Ask the children to make five decimal numbers for each line and write them in the boxes provided, then put them in the correct places along the line.

Conclude the lesson by drawing another number line on the flip chart, marked in tenths from 1.0 to 2.0. Ask: *Where will 1.2 go? What about 1.4? What about 1.25?* Explain that the 5 in 1.25 means that it should go halfway between 1.2 and 1.3.

ASSESSMENT
Note whether the children fill in the sheet correctly.

IDEAS FOR DISPLAY
Put up a number line which shows one-place decimal numbers. At the start or end of a lesson, ask the class to count out loud along the line.

IDEAS FOR DIFFERENTIATION
Less able children could start with a number line from 0 to 1 and just roll the dice for tenths, then use a number line from 0 to 2. More able children could use a set of digit cards 0–9 for whole numbers, and order on a blank number line.

TWO DECIMAL PLACES

GROUP SIZE AND ORGANIZATION
Whole class.
DURATION
20–25 minutes.
LEARNING OBJECTIVE
To order decimal numbers with up to two decimal places.

YOU WILL NEED
The number grid poster, a length of string, a marker pen, cards (about A5 size), clothes pegs.

WHAT TO DO
Hang up the string to make a 'blank' number line. Read each of the 'decimal numbers' in the lower section of the poster. Remind the children to read 73.57 as 'seventy-three point five seven', not 'seventy-three point fifty-seven'. Write each number on a piece of card and peg the cards to the number line (make sure that they are not in order).
◆ *Are they in the right order?*

◆ *How can we put them in order?*
◆ *How do you know that number goes there?*
Make sure the children understand that 73.57 is smaller than 73.7, since the number in the tenths column is smaller in 73.57.

When the numbers are in order, ask the children (working in pairs) to think of a decimal number that could go on this number line (but not at either end) and write it on a blank card. It can be a one-place or a two-place decimal. Ask children, one at a time, to put their numbers on the number line. Each time, ask the class whether they agree with the position chosen.

ASSESSMENT
Note which children think of appropriate numbers and place them correctly on the number line.

IDEAS FOR DISPLAY
Keep the number line up on display and use it in oral questioning sessions to practise mental maths skills. It can be used (with different numbers) for ordering numbers, counting along and mental calculation.

IDEAS FOR DIFFERENTIATION
Less able children could work with fewer numbers and/or with numbers to one decimal place. More able children could go on to work with numbers to three decimal places.

MORE ORDERING TO TWO DECIMAL PLACES

GROUP SIZE AND ORGANIZATION
Pairs, then groups of four.
DURATION
20–25 minutes.
LEARNING OBJECTIVES
To order decimal numbers with two decimal places.

YOU WILL NEED
For each pair: a copy of photocopiable page 29, a ten-sided dice numbered 0–9 (or a set of digit cards 0–9), scissors, pens or pencils. A flip chart and marker pen (or chalkboard and chalk).

WHAT TO DO
Pass a ten-sided dice around the room, asking the children to take turns to roll it. (Alternatively, you could

RESOURCE BANK

ORDERING DECIMALS

use a pack of digit cards.) From each three numbers rolled (for example, 3, 7 and 2), make a number with two decimal places (for example, 3.72) and write it on the flip chart. When you have ten numbers, tell the children that you are going to put them in order.
◆ *Which number is the smallest?*
◆ *How do you know?*
Encourage the children to look at the units column, then the tenths and finally the hundredths when ordering the numbers.

When all the numbers are in order, give out copies of photocopiable page 29. Ask the children in each pair to take turns at rolling the dice and filling in the boxes. When they have completed the sheet, they should cut out the numbers and put them in order from the smallest to the largest. If they finish early, they can combine their set of numbers with another pair's and order the double set together.

At the end of the session, ask a pair to say which was their smallest number and hold it up.
◆ *Did anybody have a smaller number?*
◆ *How do you know it is smaller?*
◆ *Does anyone have a number even smaller than that?*
◆ *What is the smallest number we could have?* (0.12)
◆ *What is the largest number we could have?* (9.87)

ASSESSMENT
Note which children can order their set of numbers correctly. Look for evidence of a logical, systematic approach.

IDEAS FOR DISPLAY
Put some of the children's numbers up on the number line, or order all of the children's numbers going around the room.

IDEAS FOR DIFFERENTIATION
Less able children could continue to work with one-place decimal numbers. Let more able children work with three-place decimal numbers and/or work with a mixed set of numbers in which the number of decimal places varies.

ORDERING TIMES

GROUP SIZE AND ORGANIZATION
Groups of 4 to 6.
DURATION
30–35 minutes.
LEARNING OBJECTIVES
To order speed figures with up to two decimal places.

YOU WILL NEED
A set of digital stopwatches.

WHAT TO DO
Ask each group to devise a set of five quick mental maths questions (using simple arithmetic with whole numbers up to 100). These must be questions that children will be able to answer quickly, without using written methods. Each group should then join with another group, and each child should be timed in seconds (to two decimal places if the stopwatches allow) performing the set of calculations. Talk to the children about making sure that their timing is accurate. (However, it is worth explaining that their own reaction times will mean that the timing is truly accurate only to the nearest second. The times given for the 100m race on the 'Olympic stadium' poster are measured by a computer using an electronic scanner.)

Let all the groups work with each other in rotation, until each group has a complete set of data for the class. The children in each group can then work together to order the set of times and decide on a way to record this clearly. When all the groups have collected, ordered and recorded their information, compare the results as a class.
◆ *Why did that group record longer times than any other?* (Perhaps they asked harder questions.)

ASSESSMENT
Note which children can order the times correctly and record their results clearly.

IDEAS FOR DISPLAY
The children could display their results in graph form: for example, as a bar chart with the time intervals 20–22 seconds, 22–24 seconds and so on.

IDEAS FOR DIFFERENTIATION
Less able children could measure and order times to the nearest second.

Name _____ Date _____

Ordering decimals

◆ Write your numbers in the boxes provided. Then mark five numbers on each number line.

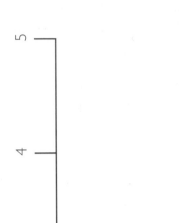
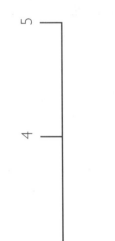

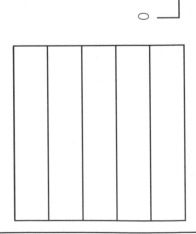
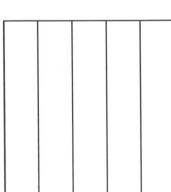

PHOTOCOPIABLE

RESOURCE BANK

Name _____   Date _____

Ordering two-place decimals

◆ Make a number to two decimal places to go in each of the blanks by rolling a ten-sided dice or picking from a set of digit cards.

Then cut out the ten decimal numbers and put them in order.

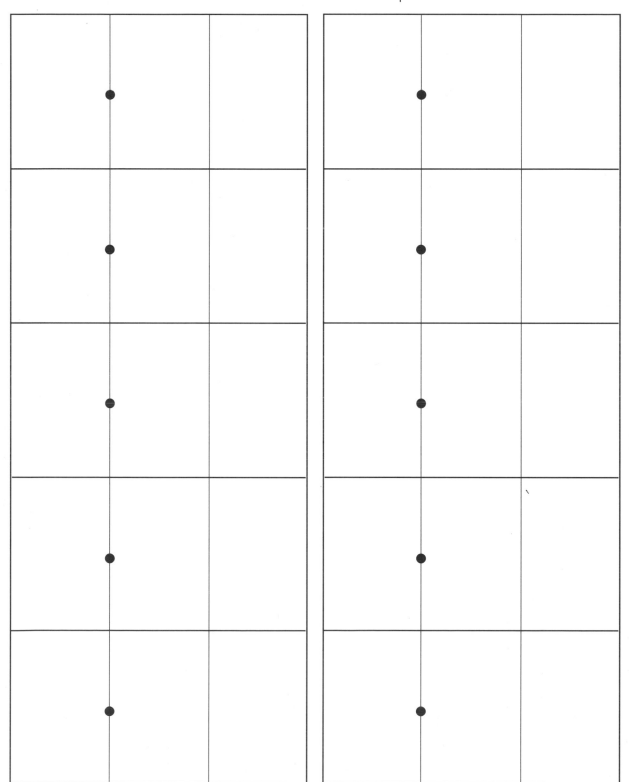

PHOTOCOPIABLE
RESOURCE
BANK

ROUNDING WITH DECIMALS

MENTAL MATHS STARTERS
◆ *Round 3.7 to the nearest whole number.*
◆ *How far is it from 2.6 to the next whole number?*
◆ *Round 3.09 to the nearest whole number.*
◆ *What is 2.78 to the nearest tenth?*
◆ *How much is it from 1.43 to the next whole number?*
◆ *What is 4.7 add 2.98 to the nearest whole number?*

ROUNDING TO NEAREST WHOLE NUMBER

GROUP SIZE AND ORGANIZATION
Whole class.
DURATION
15–20 minutes.
LEARNING OBJECTIVE
To round decimals to the nearest whole number.

YOU WILL NEED
The 'Olympic stadium' poster, cards marked with arrows (see Figure 3), a flip chart and marker pen (or chalkboard and chalk).

WHAT TO DO
Ask a child to find a decimal number on the 'Olympic stadium' poster and write it on the flip chart (for example, 9.72).
◆ *Which two whole numbers does it lie in between?*
◆ *Which one is it closer to?*
◆ *Where on the number line would it go? Closer to 9 or to 10?*
◆ *Which other number on the poster starts with 9 but is actually closer to 10?*
◆ *Which other numbers on the poster are close to 10?*
◆ *Who can think of a number that isn't on the poster and can be rounded to 10?*
◆ *Numbers that can be rounded to 10 as the nearest whole number are always between which two numbers?* (9.50 and 10.49.)
Ask someone to choose a decimal number from another section of the poster and repeat the process above. Give each child a card with an arrow on it. Point to each of the numbers on the poster in turn; ask the children to point their arrows up or down to show which way the number should be rounded.

Figure 3

ASSESSMENT
Note which children recognize whether a number should be rounded up or rounded down to the nearest whole number.

IDEAS FOR DISPLAY
Put an arrow on each number on the string number line to show whether it rounds to the previous whole number or the next whole number. (See Figure 4.)

IDEAS FOR DIFFERENTIATION
Less able children could start by working with one-place decimal numbers, and count along a number line to see which whole number each decimal number is closer to. More able children could work out how far it is to the **nearest** and to the **next** whole number (for example, 3.26 is 0.26 from the nearest whole number, but 0.74 from the next).

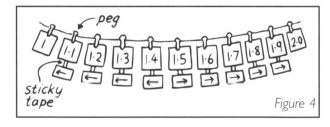

Figure 4

ROUNDING FROM 1 TO 10

GROUP SIZE AND ORGANIZATION
Whole class, then pairs.
DURATION
25–30 minutes.
LEARNING OBJECTIVE
To round two-place decimal numbers to the nearest whole number.

YOU WILL NEED
A flip chart and marker pen (or chalkboard and chalk), Blu-Tack. For each pair: a set of digit cards 0–9, paper, pens or pencils.

ROUNDING WITH DECIMALS

WHAT TO DO

Write the numbers 1–10 down the side of the flip chart. Ask a child to come up and pick three digit cards. Attach these to the flip chart with Blu-Tack in order to make a two-place decimal number (such as 6.32). Ask: *Which whole number is that nearest to?* Write the number next to 6. Repeat with other sets of three cards. If the number made rounds to a whole number that already has a decimal number next to it, rearrange the digits.

Ask the children to try this activity on paper as a game, working in pairs and taking turns. They should only write down their own numbers, not their partner's. If necessary, they can rearrange the digit cards. If a child cannot make a number that rounds to any of the whole numbers left, he or she misses a turn. The winner is the first player to have written a decimal number next to all the numbers 1–10.

At the end of the session, ask the children:
◆ *Which whole numbers do you still have left?*
◆ *Is there a pattern to the rounding?* (All numbers ending .00–.49 are rounded down, all numbers ending .50–.99 are rounded up.)
◆ *Could you make any numbers that can't be rounded to a number on the page?* (Any number less than 0.5.)

ASSESSMENT

Note which children use appropriate strategies to make numbers that can be rounded to a given whole number.

IDEAS FOR DISPLAY

The children can write a whole number on a circle of coloured paper; around the circle, on 'petals' of different-coloured paper, they can write decimal numbers that round to that whole number.

IDEAS FOR DIFFERENTIATION

Less able children could work with one-place decimals, picking pairs of cards. More able children could work with three-place decimals. They could also try rounding to numbers 1–20, or rounding to one-place decimals.

EXTENSION IDEAS

Let the children try adding pairs of decimals to give totals that can be rounded to a given number. Using the numbers from the main activity, ask the children to find as many different ways as they can of making a total that rounds to 10. The numbers having already been rounded will help them with their calculations. They can add more than two numbers if they wish. Discuss their strategies, encouraging them to estimate and to calculate mentally.

ROUNDING TO TENTHS

GROUP SIZE AND ORGANIZATION
Whole class, then individuals.
DURATION
10–15 minutes discussion, 20 minutes activity.
LEARNING OBJECTIVE
To round two-place decimals to a given tenth.

YOU WILL NEED

The number grid poster, a flip chart and marker pen (or chalkboard and chalk). For each child: a copy of photocopiable page 32, a set of digit cards 0–9.

WHAT TO DO

Draw a number line from 71.8–73.8, marked in tenths, on the flip chart. Read out the 'decimal numbers' listed on the number grid poster, and look at the number 72.86. Ask a child to come up and point to the two tenths this number lies between on the number line.
◆ *Is it closer to 72.8 or 72.9? How do you know? How many hundredths is it from 72.9?* (Count on in hundredths as a class.)
Repeat this process with the other decimal numbers. Ask the children to say together which tenth each number rounds to. Talk about the difference between the **nearest** tenth and the **next** tenth.

Now write 17.1, 21.2, 12.7 and 11.7 on the flip chart. Ask the children to arrange the digits 1, 1, 2 and 7 to make two-place decimal numbers that round to each of these numbers. *How could you check your answers? Do you know what numbers any number that can be rounded to 17.1 must lie between?*

Give out copies of photocopiable page 32 and sets of digit cards. Explain the task. The last two sections have been left blank for numbers they have chosen.

Go through the children's answers with the class.

ASSESSMENT

Note which children can round a given number to the nearest tenth and calculate how far it is from the nearest tenth. Note which children are able to find numbers that round to a given tenth.

IDEAS FOR DIFFERENTIATION

Reinforce this work with less able children by using an appropriate number line divided into tenths and hundredths, counting along the line to find out which tenth each number is closest to. More able children could work with three-place decimal numbers and round to the nearest tenth or hundredth.

Name _____   Date _____

Rounding to a tenth

◆ Look at the numbers in the small boxes on each row. Use the digits in the left-hand column to make a decimal number that can be rounded to each of the four given numbers in the same row. You must use all of the digits for each number.

The first decimal number has been found for you.

2 6 4 2	22.6	26.2	64.2	42.6
	22.64			
3 1 4 7	13.7	14.4	34.2	31.5
6 1 3 5	16.4	13.6	15.6	31.7
9 5 3 7	37.6	75.4	39.6	53.8
8 2 3 6	23.7	26.4	28.6	32.9

◆ In the last two rows, write four digits of your own choice in the left-hand column and use them to make some two decimal place numbers. Round each of the numbers you make to the nearest tenth. For example:

| 9 7 6 5 | |
| | |

| 9 7 6 5 | |
| | 57.89 |

| 9 7 6 5 | 57.7 |
| | 57.89 |

PHOTOCOPIABLE
RESOURCE BANK